Songbird Eva C

Wise Publications
London/New York/Sydney/Paris/Copenhagen/Madrid/Tokyo

Fields Of Gold

Words & Music by Sting

years have passed since those sum-mer days a-mong the fields of bar-ley.

See the chil-dren run as the sun goes down as you lie in fields of gold. You'll re-mem-ber me when the west wind moves a-mong the fields of bar-ley. You

Wade In The Water

Traditional, arranged by Eva Cassidy.

God's gon-na trou-ble the wa - - - ter.

%

1. Who's that young girl dressed in red wade in the
(Verses 2 & 3 see block lyrics)

wa - ter?__ Must be the chil - dren that Mo - ses__ led.__

God's gon-na trou-ble the wa - - ter, oh.

Verse 2:
Who's that young girl dressed in white
Wade in the water
Must be the children of the Israelite
Oh, God's gonna trouble the water.

Wade in the water *etc.*

Verse 3:
Who's that young girl dressed in blue
Wade in the water
Must be the children that's coming through
God's gonna trouble the water.

Wade in the water *etc.*

Wayfaring Stranger

Traditional, arranged by Eva Cassidy.

16

⊕ *Coda*

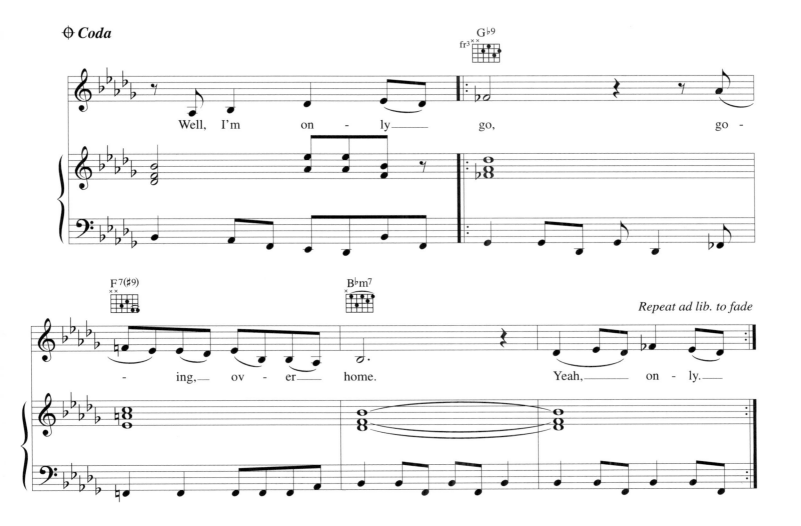

Verse 2:
I know dark clouds
Will gather on me
I know my way
My way is rough and steep
Yeah, and beautiful fields
Lie just before me
And God's redeem
Their vigils keep.

I'm going there to see my Father etc.

Verse 3:
I want to wear
That crown of glory
When I get home
To that good land
Well, I want to shout
Salvation's story
In concert with
All the blood-washed band.

I'm going there to see my Saviour etc.

19

Autumn Leaves

Original Words by Jacques Prevert. Music by Joseph Kosma.
English Words by Johnny Mercer.

Songbird

Words & Music by Christine McVie.

2. To_____ you___

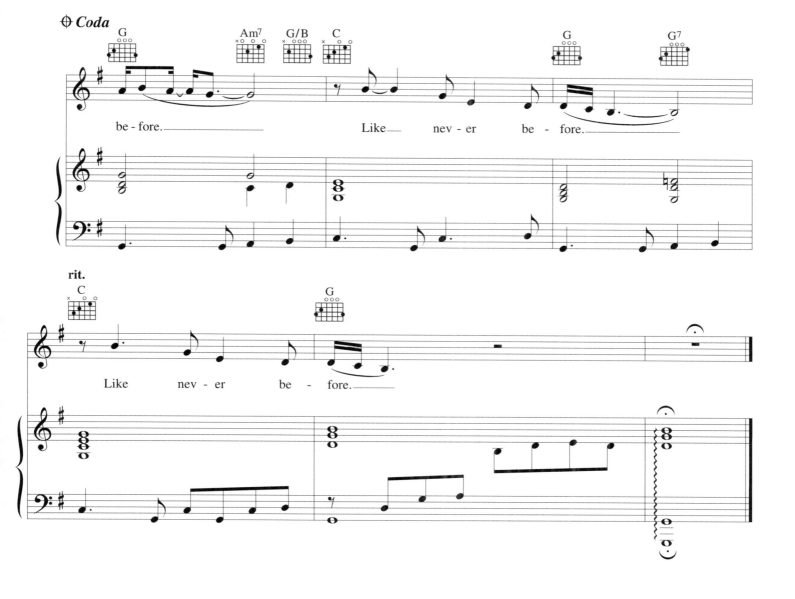

Verse 2:
To you I would give the world
To you I'd never be cold
Cos I feel that when I'm with you
It's alright
I know it's right.

And the songbirds keep singing *etc.*

Time Is A Healer

Words & Music by Diane Scanlon & Greg Smith.

if time is a heal - er,_____ mm,____ mm,____

(Then all hearts that____ break._____)
then all_____ hearts that break_____

are put back____ to - geth - er a - gain_____ cos

1.
love heals_____ the wound it makes.____

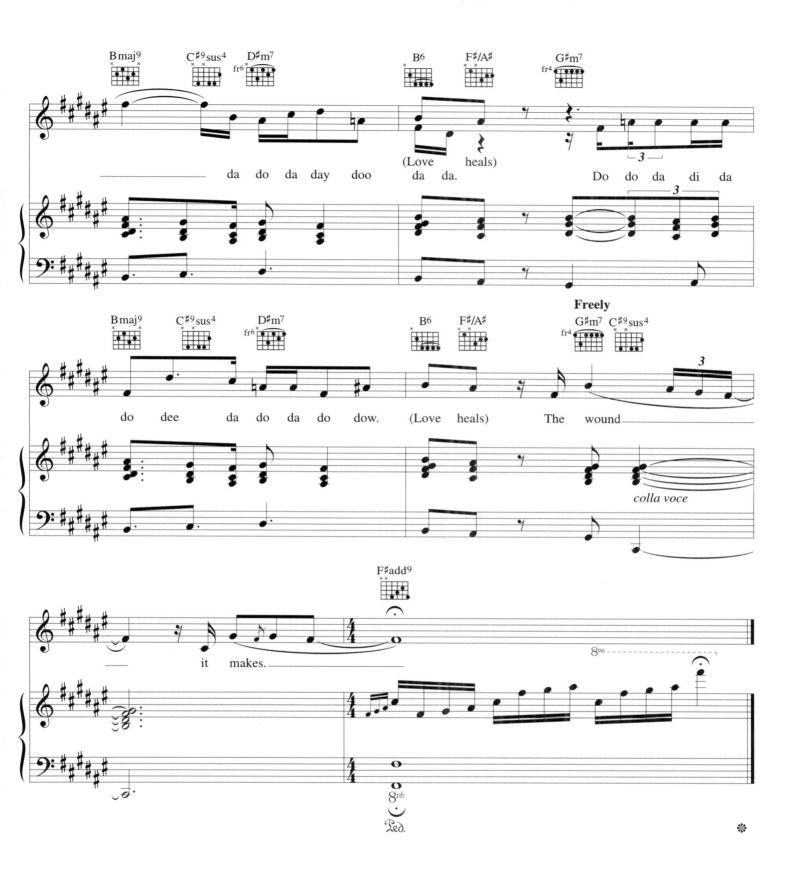

Verse 2:
I spoke such harsh words before our goodbye
Well I wanted to hurt you for the tears you made
You made me cry
All my hopes and dreams, well they started vanishing
Those tender hurt feelings became a dangerous thing.

Oh, if time is a healer *etc.*

I Know You By Heart

Words & Music by Diane Scanlon & Eve Nelson.

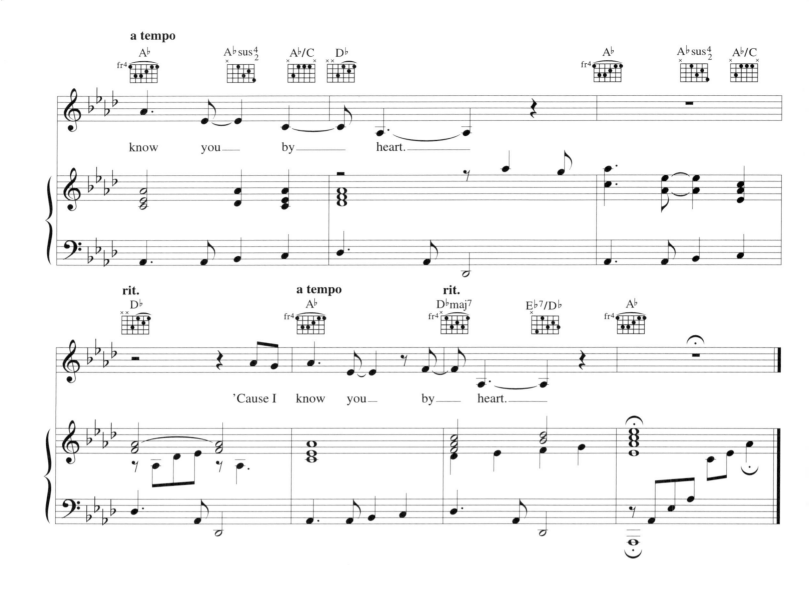

Verse 2:
Mornings in April
Sharing our secrets
We'd walk on till the morning was gone
We were like children
Laughing for hours
The joy you gave me lives on and on.

'Cause I know you by heart.

Verse 3:
You left in Autumn
The leaves were turning
I walked down roads of orange and gold
I saw your sweet smile
I heard your laughter
You're still here beside me every day.

'Cause I know you by heart.

People Get Ready

Words & Music by Curtis Mayfield.

1. Peo-ple get rea-dy,____ there's a train a-com-ing.
(Verses 2 & 3 see block lyrics)

Yeah, —— yeah, yeah.

D.%. al Coda

3. Now

Coda

—— Peo - ple get rea - dy there's a train —— a - com - ing. ——

43

Verse 2:
People, get ready for the train to Jordan
Picking up passengers from coast to coast
Faith is the key, open the doors and board them
There's room for all of the love and honesty.

Verse 3:
Now there ain't no room for the hopeless sinner
Who's hard on mankind just to save his own
Have pity on those whose chances are thinner
'Cause there's no hiding place from the King on his throne.

Oh, Had I A Golden Thread

Words & Music by Pete Seeger.

rain - - - bow___ de - sign.

Hammond Organ

ad lib.

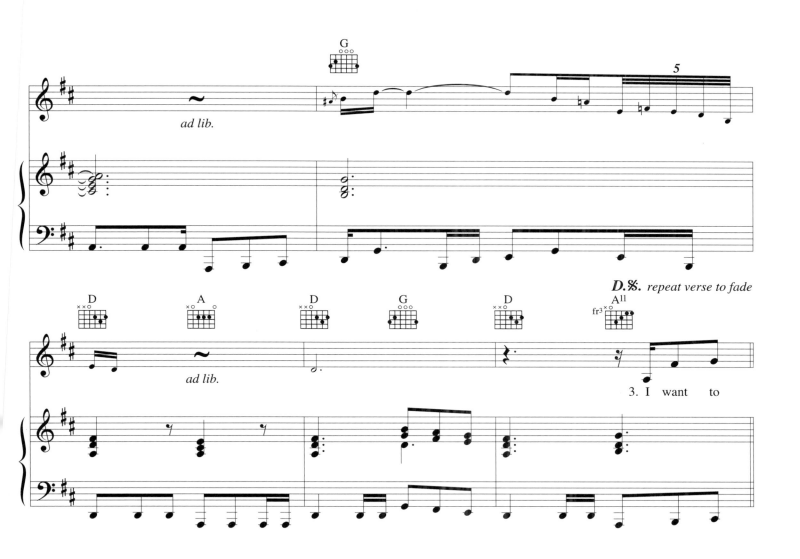

Verse 2:
In it I would weave the courage of women giving birth
And in it I would weave the innocence of the children of all the earth
Children of all the earth.

Verse 3:
I want to show my brothers and sisters my rainbow design
 Cause I would bind up this sorry world
With my hand and my heart and mind
Oh, hand and heart and mind.

Verse 4:
Oh, had I a golden thread and a needle so fine
I would weave a magic spell
Of a rainbow design
Of a rainbow design.

Verse 5:
Ad lib to fade.

Over The Rainbow

Words by E.Y. Harburg
Music by Harold Arlen

Verse 2:
Somewhere over the rainbow
Skies are blue
And the dreams that you dared to dream
Really do come true.

01/06 (57450)

Exclusive distributors:
Music Sales Limited
8/9 Frith Street, London W1V 5TZ, England.
Music Sales Pty Limited
120 Rothschild Avenue, Rosebery, NSW 2018,
Australia.

Order No.AM970981
ISBN 0-7119-8931-1
This book © Copyright 2001 by Wise Publications.

Music arranged by Derek Jones.
Music engraved by Paul Ewers Music Design.

Cover photograph courtesy of Hot Records.

Printed in the United Kingdom by
Printwise (Haverhill) Limited, Suffolk.

Your Guarantee of Quality:
As publishers, we strive to produce every
book to the highest commercial standards.
The music has been freshly engraved and, whilst endeavouring
to retain the original running order of the recorded album,
the book has been carefully designed to minimise awkward
page turns and to make playing from it a real pleasure.
Particular care has been given to specifying acid-free,
neutral-sized paper made from pulps which have not been
elemental chlorine bleached.
This pulp is from farmed sustainable forests and was produced
with special regard for the environment.
Throughout, the printing and binding have been planned
to ensure a sturdy, attractive publication which should give
years of enjoyment.
If your copy fails to meet our high standards, please inform
us and we will gladly replace it.

Music Sales' complete catalogue describes thousands
of titles and is available in full colour sections by subject,
direct from Music Sales Limited.
Please state your areas of interest and send a cheque/
postal order for £1.50 for postage to: Music Sales Limited,
Newmarket Road, Bury St. Edmunds, Suffolk IP33 3YB.

www.musicsales.com